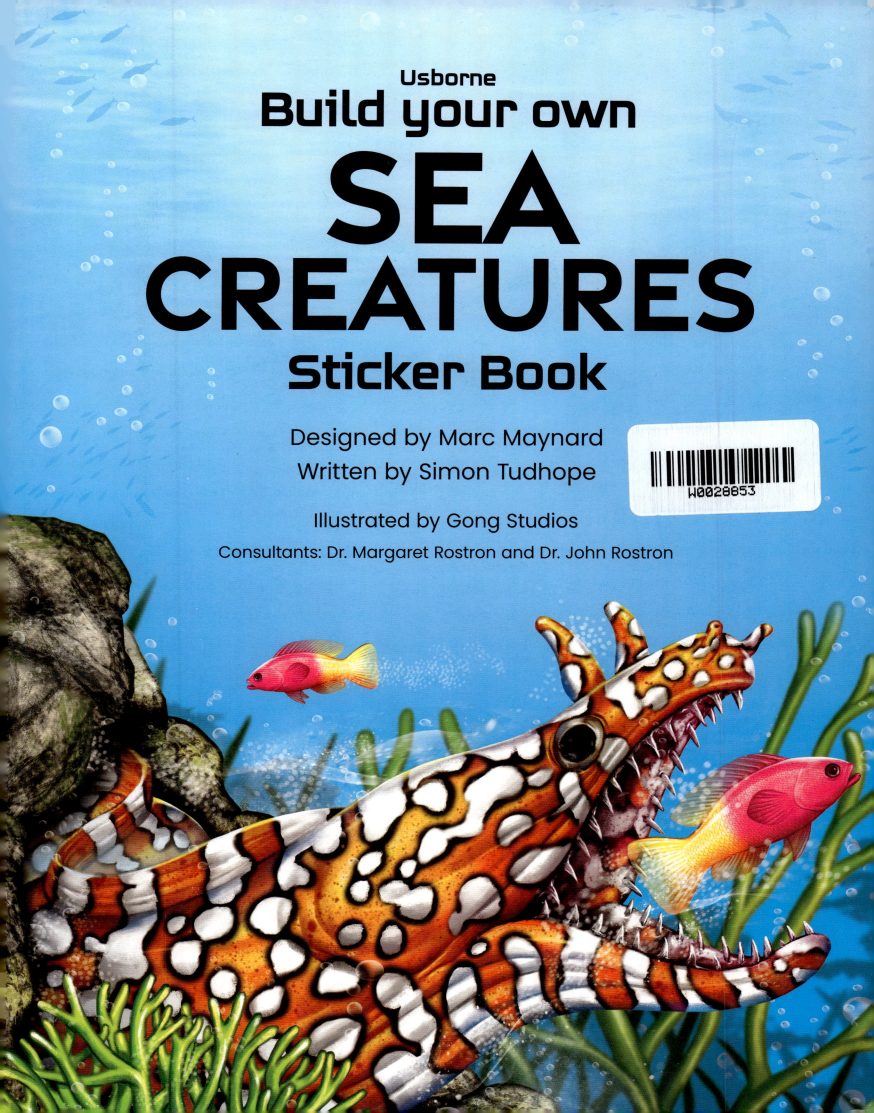

HUMPBACK WHALE

These ocean giants are feeding in the freezing waters off the Alaskan coast. The males sing long, haunting songs that can be felt by other whales thousands of miles away.

STATISTICS
- **SCIENTIFIC NAME:** *Megaptera novaeangliae*
- **LIVES:** worldwide
- **DIET:** krill, fish
- **SIZE:** 16m (52ft) long
- **LIFESPAN:** 50 years

GIANT PACIFIC OCTOPUS

This amazing creature has nine brains – a small one at the top of each arm and a large one in the middle. With all that brainpower it can figure out how to smash open clam shells with stones, or even twist the lid off a jam jar.

STATISTICS

- **SCIENTIFIC NAME:** *Enteroctopus dofleini*
- **LIVES:** North Pacific Ocean
- **DIET:** shrimp, clams, lobsters, fish
- **SIZE:** 6m (20ft) armspan
- **LIFESPAN:** 5 years

MAUVE STINGER JELLYFISH

These creatures have no brain, no heart and no lungs. They swarm in their thousands, and use their long, stinger-covered tentacles to catch their food. At night, you can see them pulsing with light, like a storm cloud drifting through the ocean.

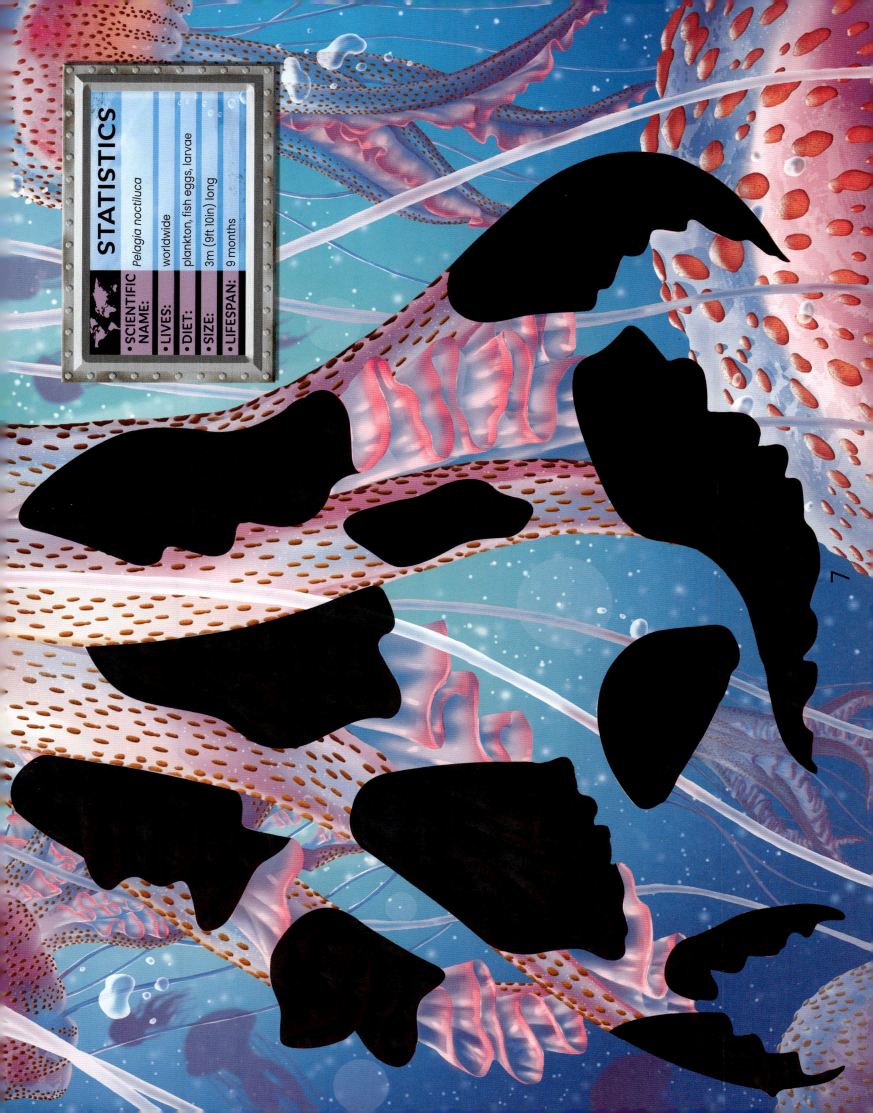

STATISTICS

- SCIENTIFIC NAME: *Pelagia noctiluca*
- LIVES: worldwide
- DIET: plankton, fish eggs, larvae
- SIZE: 3m (9ft 10in) long
- LIFESPAN: 9 months

RED LIONFISH

Despite its shape and size, this lionfish is one of the stealthiest hunters in the reef. Spreading its fins to hide the swish of its tail, it inches towards its prey. The smaller fish just doesn't spot the danger. Or not until it's too late...

STATISTICS	
• SCIENTIFIC NAME:	*Pterois volitans*
• LIVES:	Indian & Pacific Oceans
• DIET:	fish, crustaceans
• SIZE:	45cm (18in)
• LIFESPAN:	10 years

ATLANTIC SAILFISH

Built for explosive speed over short distances, this is one of the fastest creatures in the ocean. It slashes though schools of fish with a rapier bill, then turns to pick off the wounded.

STATISTICS

- **SCIENTIFIC NAME:** *Istiophorus albicans*
- **LIVES:** Atlantic Ocean
- **DIET:** fish, squid, crustaceans
- **SIZE:** 3.4m (11ft)
- **LIFESPAN:** 5 years

DRAGON MORAY EEL

Nothing escapes this ambush predator. It clamps onto its prey with needle-like teeth, then a second jaw emerges to drag the fish down into its throat.

STATISTICS

- **SCIENTIFIC NAME:** Enchelycore pardalis
- **LIVES:** Indian & Pacific Oceans
- **DIET:** fish, small octopuses, squid
- **SIZE:** 90cm (35in)
- **LIFESPAN:** 5 years

LONG-SNOUTED SEAHORSE

It's the male seahorse that gives birth, not the female. She puts hundreds of eggs inside his pouch, and there the babies grow. He swells and swells over several weeks, then squirts them all into the sea.

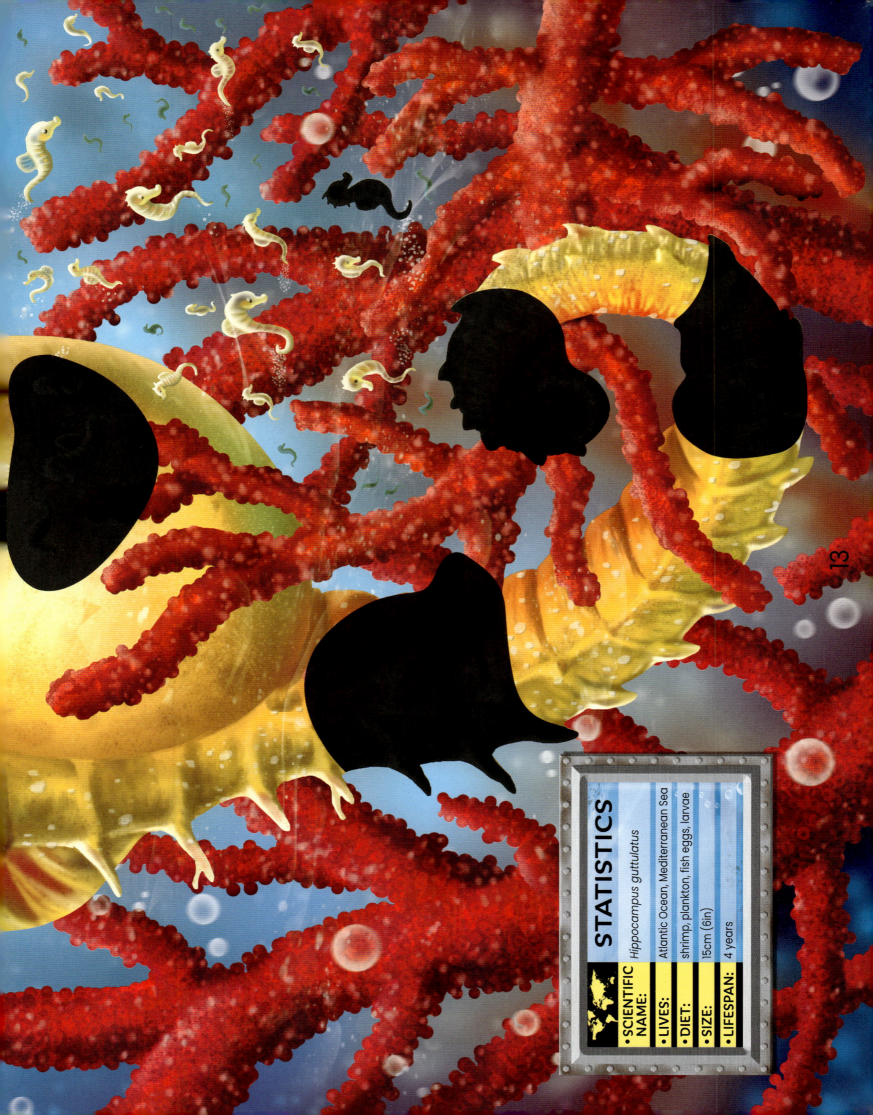

STATISTICS

- SCIENTIFIC NAME: *Hippocampus guttulatus*
- LIVES: Atlantic Ocean, Mediterranean Sea
- DIET: shrimp, plankton, fish eggs, larvae
- SIZE: 15cm (6in)
- LIFESPAN: 4 years

SCALLOPED HAMMERHEAD SHARK

This shark has one of the most sophisticated surveillance systems on the planet. Its eyes are positioned to see above and below at the same time, and its head is lined with electroreceptors that can pinpoint the beating of a fish's heart – even when buried under sand.

STATISTICS

• SCIENTIFIC NAME:	*Sphyrna lewini*
• LIVES:	worldwide
• DIET:	fish, squid, octopuses
• SIZE:	4m (13ft)
• LIFESPAN:	30 years

GREEN SEA TURTLE

This turtle is on a thousand-mile journey back to the place where she was born. There she'll dig a nest in the warm sand and lay her eggs. Nine weeks later, a hundred little hatchlings will make their way down the beach and into the sea.

STATISTICS

- **SCIENTIFIC NAME:** *Chelonia mydas*
- **LIVES:** worldwide
- **DIET:** adults eat algae & seagrass
- **SIZE:** 1.5m (5ft)
- **LIFESPAN:** 50 years

GREAT BARRACUDA

This ferocious killer is called the 'ocean wolf' because it can hunt in packs. It herds schools of fish into shallow water, before shredding them with fang-like teeth.

	STATISTICS
• SCIENTIFIC NAME:	*Sphyraena barracuda*
• LIVES:	worldwide
• DIET:	fish, octopuses, squid
• SIZE:	1.5m (5ft)
• LIFESPAN:	14 years

MANDARINFISH

This fish may look pretty, but its bright skin is actually a warning sign to predators lurking nearby. It means: "Watch out! I'm covered in a smelly, toxic goo and eating me would do you no good!"

STATISTICS

- **SCIENTIFIC NAME:** *Synchiropus splendidus*
- **LIVES:** Pacific Ocean
- **DIET:** small crustaceans, worms, snails
- **SIZE:** 7cm (3in)
- **LIFESPAN:** 10 years

HUMPBACK ANGLERFISH

Two miles down, this creature drifts through the black depths. A bright lure dangles over its cavernous mouth — a small, blinking light that fascinates the curious shrimp...

STATISTICS

- **SCIENTIFIC NAME:** *Melanocetus johnsonii*
- **LIVES:** worldwide
- **DIET:** deep-sea fish, shrimp
- **SIZE:** female: 15cm (6in) male: 3cm (1in)
- **LIFESPAN:** unknown

SALLY LIGHTFOOT CRAB

This coastal scavenger needs to be light on its feet to avoid predators. Leaping from boulder to boulder and scrabbling up vertical rocks, it darts over the shore like a ten-legged gymnast.

STATISTICS	
• SCIENTIFIC NAME:	*Grapsus grapsus*
• LIVES:	Pacific coast of C. & S. America
• DIET:	algae, plants, dead animals
• SIZE:	12cm (5in)
• LIFESPAN:	5 years

GLOSSARY

- **ALGAE:** water plants
- **CAVERNOUS:** large, cave-like space
- **CRUSTACEAN:** an animal with a hard shell and several pairs of legs, such as a crab or shrimp
- **ELECTRORECEPTORS:** organs that detect electricity
- **HATCHLING:** an animal that has just hatched from an egg
- **KRILL:** small crustaceans, similar to shrimp
- **LARVAE:** young animals such as fish or insects that haven't yet changed into their adult form
- **LURE:** an object that attracts prey
- **PLANKTON:** a mass of tiny animals and plants that drifts near the surface of the ocean
- **RAPIER:** a long, thin sword
- **SCHOOL:** a group of fish swimming together
- **SURVEILLANCE:** watching or searching
- **TOXIC:** poisonous

Edited by Sam Taplin
Research by Kate Nolan
Digital manipulation by Keith Furnival

First published in 2022 by Usborne Publishing Ltd, Usborne House, 83-85 Saffron Hill, London EC1N 8RT, England. usborne.com
Copyright © 2022 Usborne Publishing Ltd. The name Usborne and the Balloon logo are trade marks of Usborne Publishing Ltd. All rights reserved.
No part of this publication may be reproduced, stored in a retrieval system or transmitted in any form or by any means without the prior permission of the publisher. UE. Printed in China.

GIANT PACIFIC OCTOPUS pages 4-5

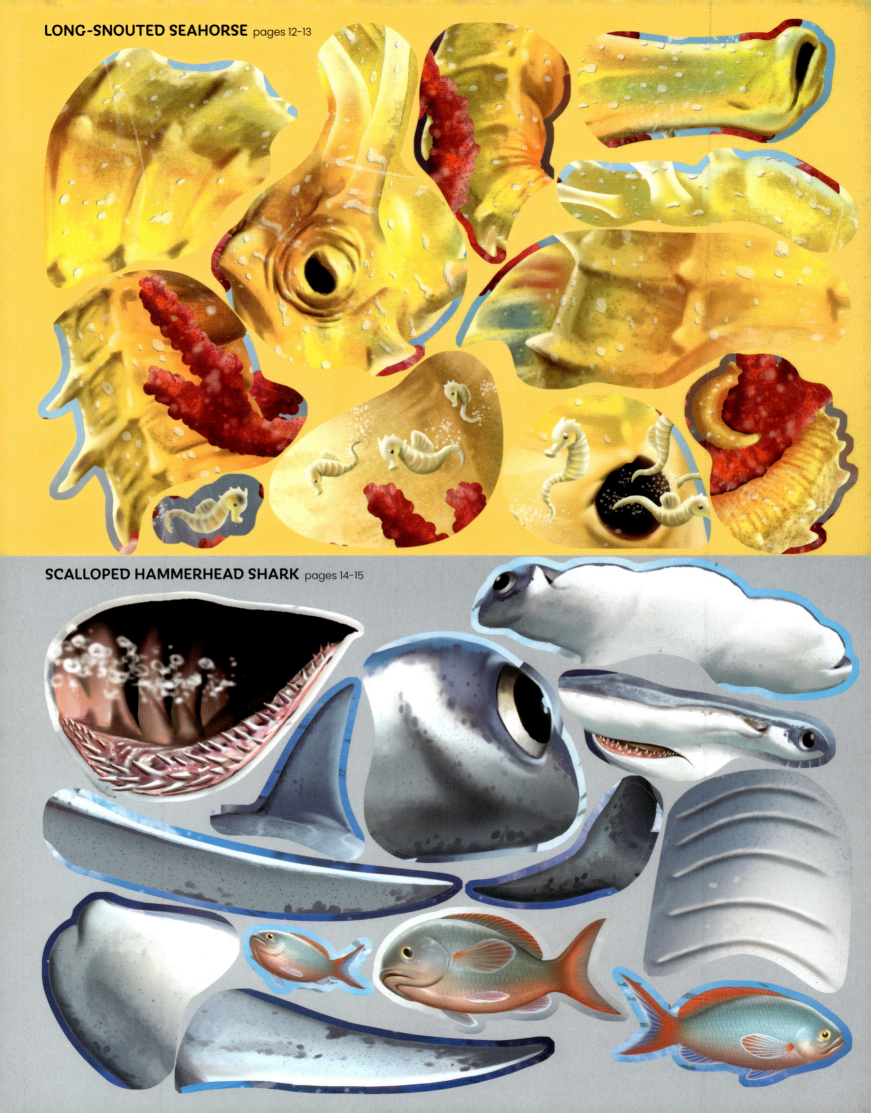
LONG-SNOUTED SEAHORSE pages 12-13

SCALLOPED HAMMERHEAD SHARK pages 14-15

GREEN SEA TURTLE pages 16-17

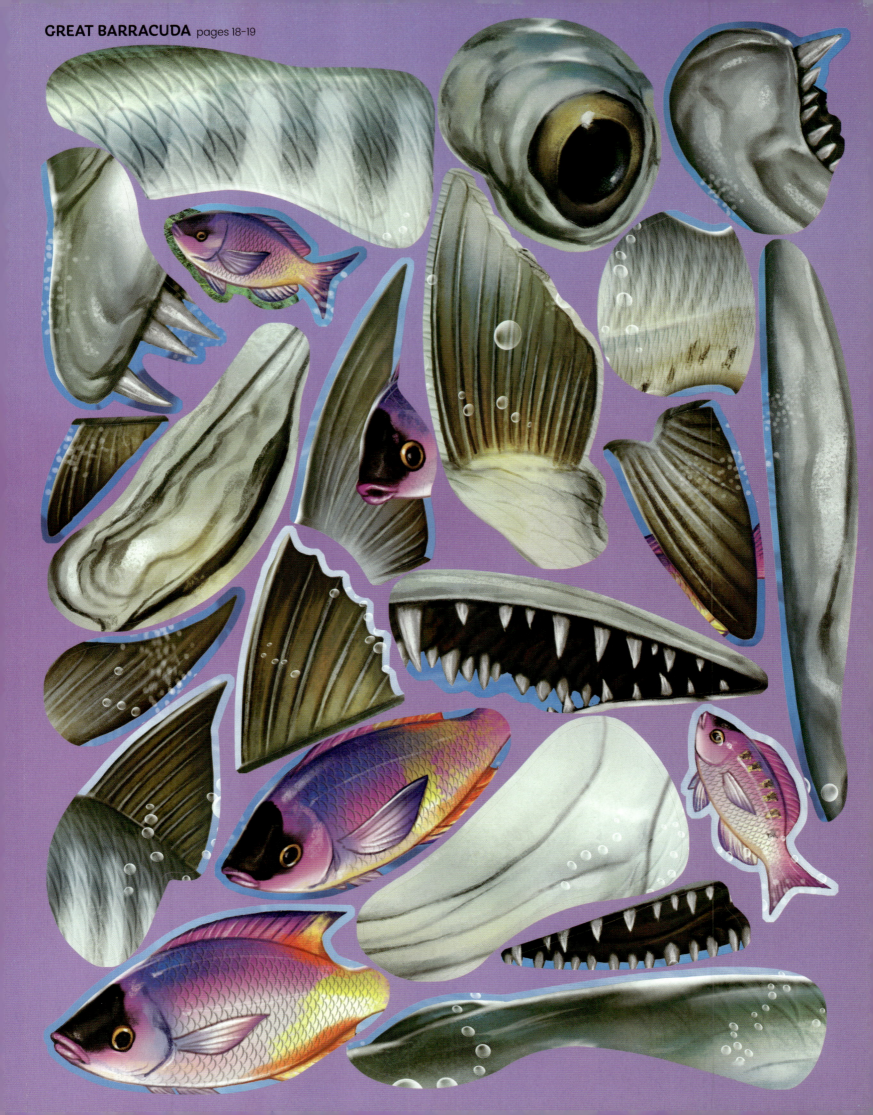

GREAT BARRACUDA pages 18-19

MANDARINFISH page 20

HUMPBACK ANGLERFISH page 21

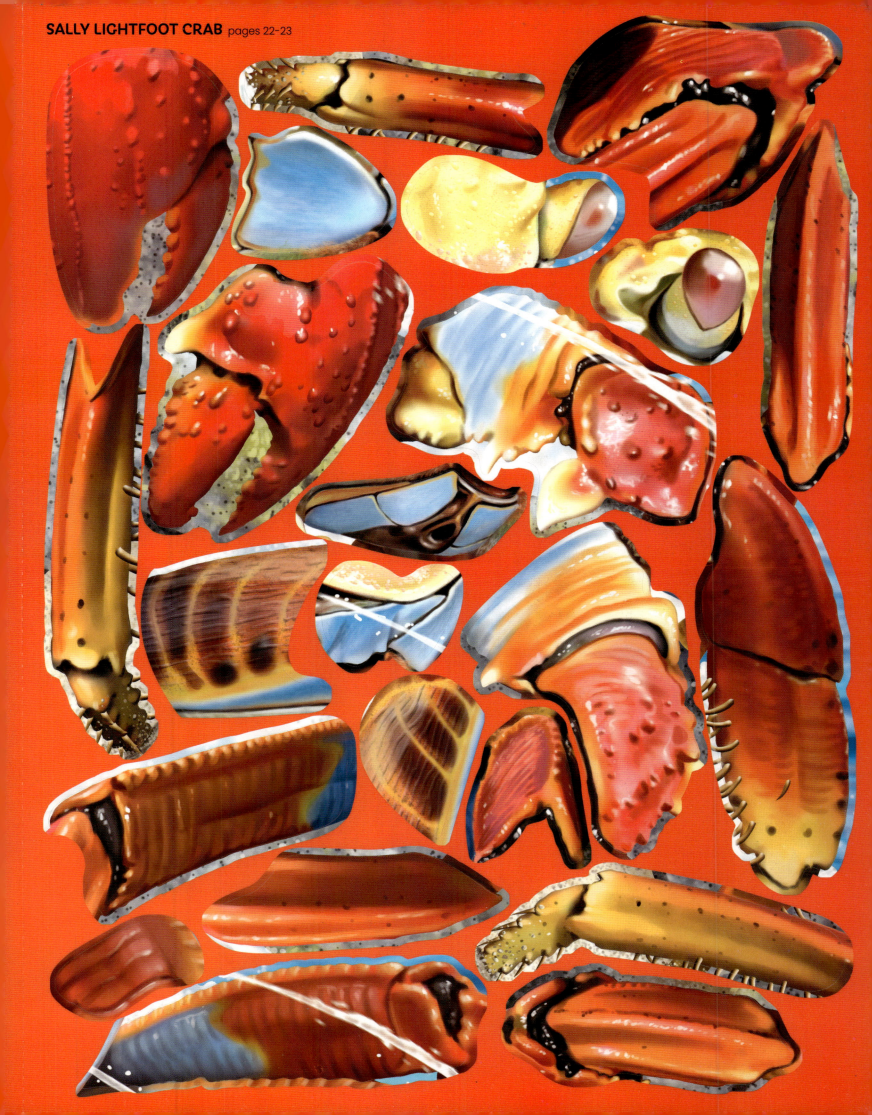
SALLY LIGHTFOOT CRAB pages 22-23